tenor
saxo

Now you ca
tenor saxoph
specially recorded

C000150283

MOVIE
HITS

TAKE
THE
LEAD

tenor
saxophone

International
MUSIC
Publications

International Music Publications Limited
Griffin House 161 Hammersmith Road London W6 8BS England

Series Editor: Sadie Cook

Editorial, production and recording: Artemis Music Limited
Design & Production: Space DPS Limited

Published 1999

International MUSIC Publications

International Music Publications Limited
Griffin House 161 Hammersmith Road London W6 8BS England

International Music Publications Limited

England: Griffin House
161 Hammersmith Road
London W6 8BS

Germany: Marstallstr. 8
D-80539 München

Denmark: Danmusik
Vognmagergade 7
DK1120 Copenhagen K

Italy: Via Campania 12
20098 San Giuliano Milanese
Milano

Spain: Magallanes 25
28015 Madrid

France: 20 Rue de la Ville-l'Eveque
75008 Paris

WARNER BROS. PUBLICATIONS U.S. INC.

USA: 15800 N.W. 48th Avenue
Miami, Florida 33014

Australia: 3 Talavera Road
North Ryde
New South Wales 2113

Scandinavia: P.O. Box 533
Vendevagen 85 B
S-182 15 Danderyd
Sweden

tenor saxophone

TAKE THE LEAD

In the Book...

On the CD...

Because You Loved Me

(from *Up Close And Personal*)

Words and Music by Diane Warren

Demonstration

Backing

Blue Monday

(from *The Wedding Singer*)

Words and Music by
Stephen Morris, Peter Hook,
Bernard Sumner and Gillian Gilbert

Demonstration   Backing

Moderately fast

(Everything I Do) I Do It For You

(from *Robin Hood: Prince of Thieves*)

Words and Music by Bryan Adams,
Robert John 'Mutt' Lange and Michael Kamen

I Don't Want To Miss A Thing

(from *Armageddon*)

Demonstration

Backing

Words and Music by Diane Warren

I Will Always Love You

(from *The Bodyguard*)

Words and Music by Dolly Parton

Demonstration   Backing

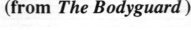

10/5/04

Demonstration

Backing

Star Wars (Main Title)

By John Williams

Moderate march tempo

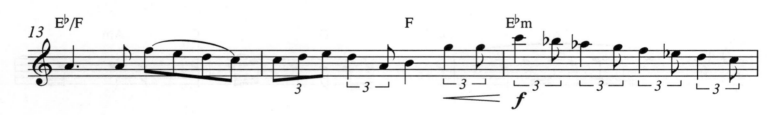

poco rall.   a tempo

più mosso

The Wind Beneath My Wings

(from *Beaches*)

Words and Music by
Larry Henley and Jeff Silbar

17/5/04

You Can Leave Your Hat On

(from *The Full Monty*)

Demonstration

Backing

Words and Music by Randy Newman

Reproduced and printed by
Halstan & Co. Ltd., Amersham, Bucks., England